TERRY MOORE
RACHEL RISING
ABSTRACT STUDIO
ISSUE No.
19
3.99 US

"BEST FRIENDS, FOREVER.
THICK OR THIN, WHATEVER.
OLD AND GRAY, FRIENDS FOR LIFE;
TO THE GRAVE AND AFTERLIFE."
—THE PACT

FLAP!
FLAP!

THAT IS A LIGHT
YOU CANNOT HIDE,
MARY McKENNA.

..|/| \/|\ TΓ∩ΓₚS IN
AFGHANISTAN...

THE DOW CLOSED
AT A RECORD HIGH...

...AND WEATHER
AT ELEVEN...

WE HAVE TO MOVE
THESE CARS!

WE'LL MATCH
ANY DEAL!

THE MAYOR SPEAKS
ABOUT THE RAT
INFESTATION...

\/\|\ \/|
\/ SHOP \/...

RACHEL?

RACHEL, THANK GOD.
I'VE BEEN WAITING...
HOPING YOU'D WAKE UP.

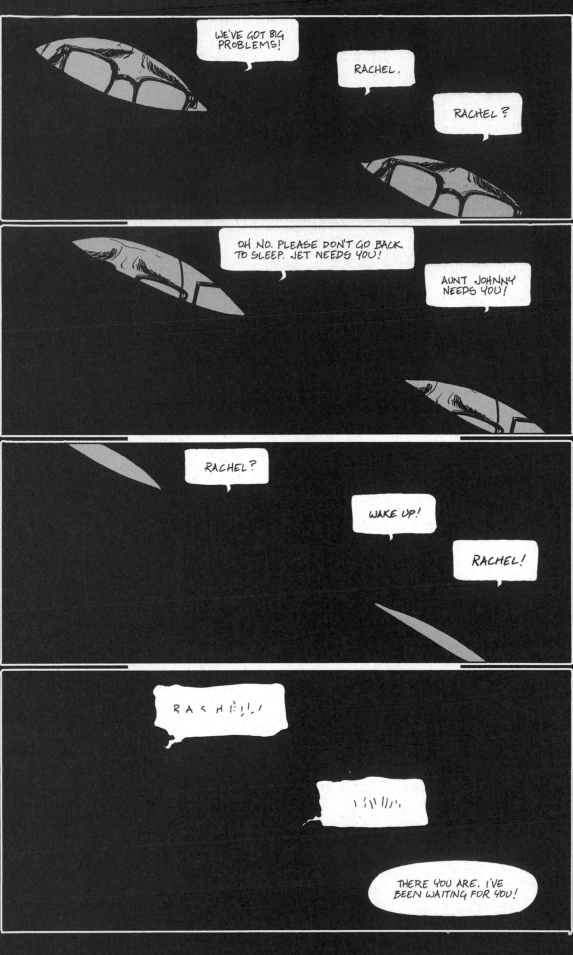

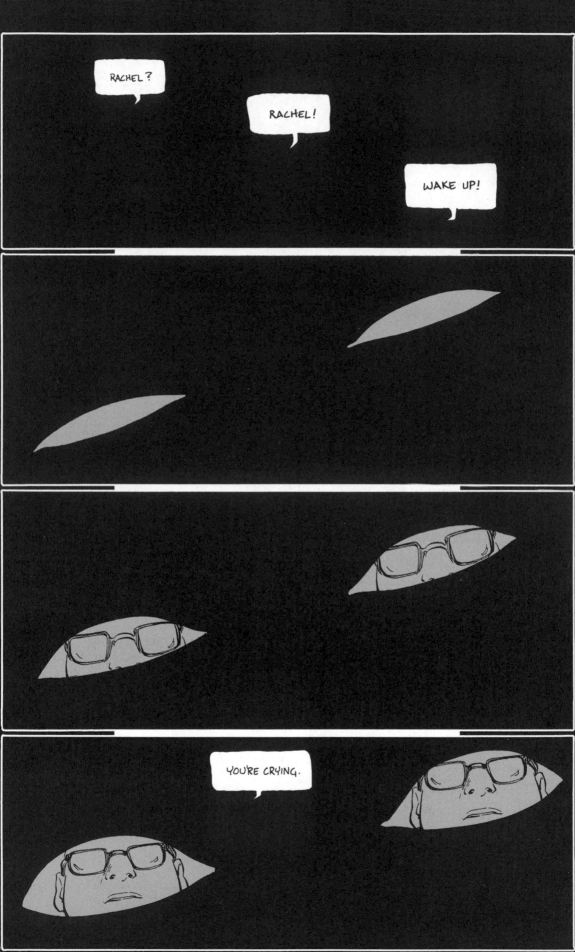

"SIX LITTLE WHORES, GLAD TO BE ALIVE,
ONE SIDLES UP TO JACK, THEN THERE ARE FIVE."
—UNKNOWN, 19TH CENTURY

ZOE?

WHAT ARE YOU DOING TO JACK?

MAKING HIM MINE.

BY FILING OFF THE POINT?

ZOE, THAT BLADE IS OLDER THAN MANKIND.

YOU GAVE HIM TO ME.

AS A CARETAKER— NOT THE OWNER. HE'S HAD MANY CARETAKERS THROUGHOUT HISTORY.

THEY'RE DEAD. HE'S MINE.

SO YOU TOOK IT UPON YOURSELF TO RESHAPE A PRICELESS ANTIQUITY INTO A BUTTER KNIFE?

I DON'T STAB... I CUT.

AND...

I CAN'T HIDE A FAT-HANDLED LONGPOINT UNDER MY CLOTHES. I PREFER TO CARRY IT FLAT AGAINST ME, LIKE THIS, UNDER MY ARM. EASY IN, EASY OUT.

OH NO.

WHAT?

SEE WHAT?!

NO! NO!

YOU DON'T SEE IT?

SHE'S LEAVING!

THEY'RE BOTH LEAVING!

SHIT!

BARK! BARK! BARK! BARK! BARK!

PRISCILLA, QUICK!!

AIIEGH!

RACHEL!

YIKE! YIKE!

WHAT ARE YOU DOING?!

RACHEL!

UURGH...

I'M AFRAID TO MOVE.

GIVE IT A MINUTE — YOU GET USED TO IT.

WHERE AM I?

MANSON. BUT THE TIME HAS CHANGED.

WHAT TIME IS IT?

TWENTY THIRTEEN.

WHAT IS THAT? HOW MANY HOURS HAVE I...

JAMES...

THAT'S THE YEAR. IT'S 2013.

NO, THAT'S IMPOSSIBLE. PLEASE... BRYN...

TELL ME THE TRUTH.

≀SIGH≀

≀CLICK!≀

...THE CBS NEWS

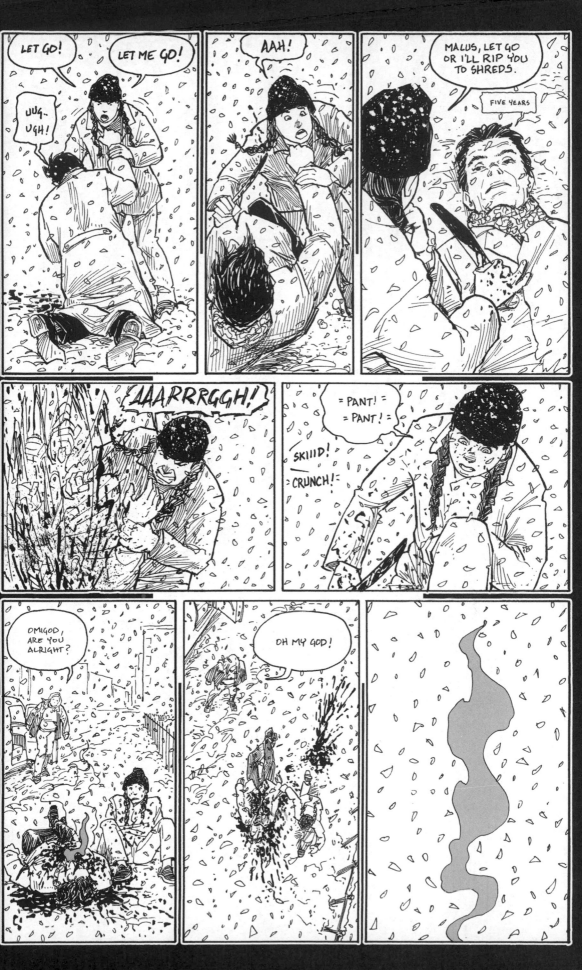

ABSTRACT STUDIO
ISSUE NO.
3.99 US

TERRY MOORE

RACHEL RISING

21

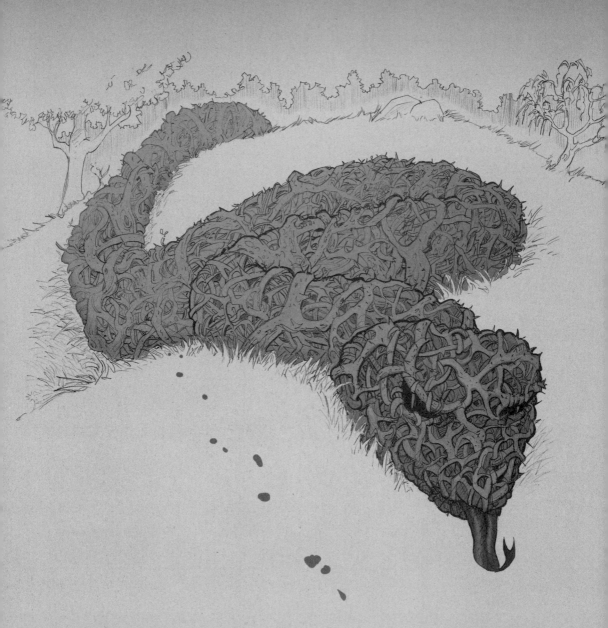

"SNOW FELL ON THE LIVING AND THE DEAD,
'TIL THEY WERE JOINED TOGETHER,
AND WINTER THEIR BED."
—LILITH'S SONG

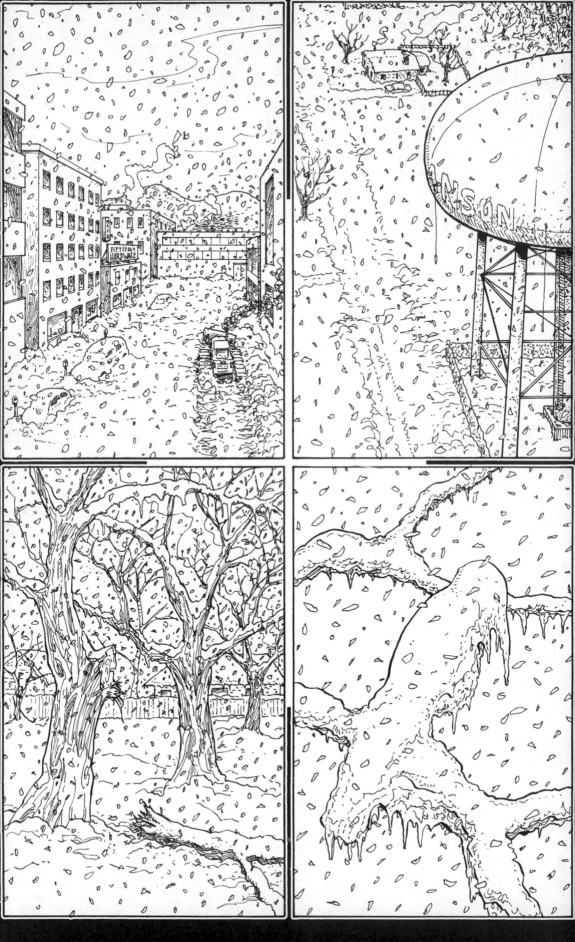

I DON'T KNOW. THERE ARE SOME PRETTY SMART PEOPLE AROUND TODAY, TOO. YOU'RE SMART.

NOT SMART ENOUGH.

I CAN'T FIX THIS. I CAN'T REVERSE DEATH.

I'VE TRIED.

AND TRIED.

AND TRIED.

DR. SIEMEN, IS IT POSSIBLE TO FLUSH THE POISON OUT OF AUNT JOHNNY'S BODY?

IT'S TOO LATE NOW. WHAT'S THE POINT?

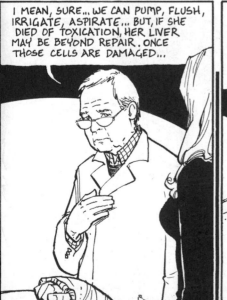

I MEAN, SURE... WE CAN PUMP, FLUSH, IRRIGATE, ASPIRATE... BUT, IF SHE DIED OF TOXICATION, HER LIVER MAY BE BEYOND REPAIR. ONCE THOSE CELLS ARE DAMAGED...

HOWEVER, THAT MIGHT EXPLAIN YOUR RECOVERY. IF CAROL USED A NON-TOXIC, LIKE WOOD ALCOHOL, IT'S HARMLESS UNTIL IT HITS THE LIVER. THEN IT CONVERTS TO FORMALDEHYDE. THE EFFECT DEPENDS ON THE INDIVIDUAL.

I WOULD VENTURE TO GUESS ALL BETS ARE OFF WITH YOU AND SYSTEMIC TOXICATION.

SUPPOSING THERE IS NO CELL DAMAGE, WHAT DO YOU PROPOSE TO DO WITH THE BODY WHEN IT'S CLEAN?

TRY TO GET HER SPIRIT TO GO BACK IN.

HER SPIRIT.

MM HMM.

I'M SORRY, RACHEL... I... I'M GETTING CONFUSED. I FIND MY DEAREST FRIEND DEAD AND... AND YOU'RE TALKING ABOUT HER SPIRIT LIKE IT'S A CAR PART. I'M NOT IN THE MOOD FOR SUCH FOOLISHNESS.

BUT...

IT'S NOT FOOLISHNESS, DR. SIEMEN. JET AND I BOTH SAW HER TRAP THE SPIRIT FROM JOHNNY'S BODY.

TRAPPED IT. HOW?

UH...

IN THE DOG.

THE DOG.

YEAH. JOHNNY'S DOG. PRISCILLA.

YOU SAW THIS WOMAN'S SPIRIT... GO INTO... A DOG.

WELL, NO. BUT I SAW ONE FREAKED OUT DOG.

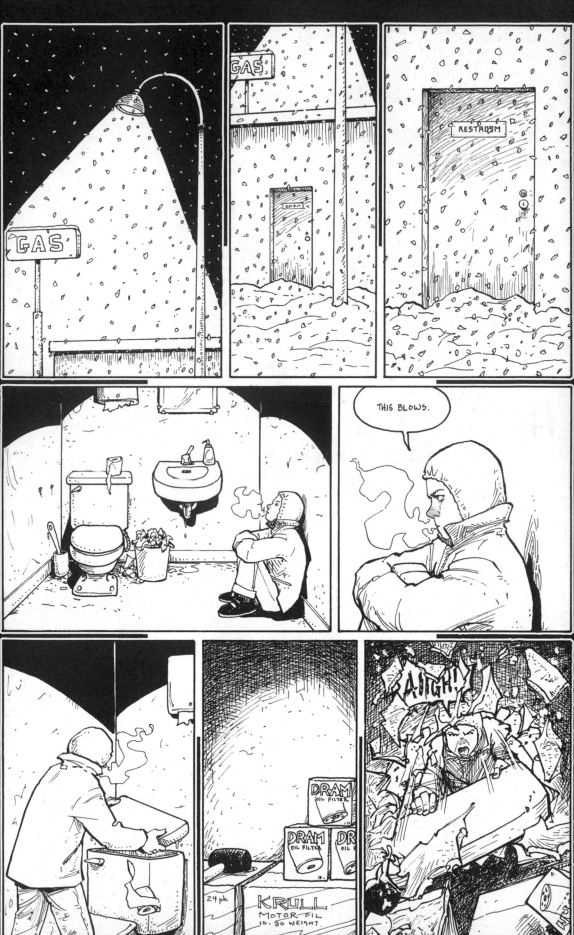

ZiiiiiP!

:SIGH:

SLAM!!

KRAK!

DON'T MAKE ME REGRET THIS,

GASP!

PANT!
PANT!

SCHLICK!

CLANG!
CLANK!

WE COOL?

GOOD.

SNAP!

CREAK!

KRAK!

WOOF! WOOF!

WOOFF! WOOFF!

SONNUVABITCH!

WOOFF!

SHUT UP, DUKE! SHUT UP!

THERE BETTER BE A DEAD BODY IN HERE OR YOU'RE STEW MEAT, YA HEAR?

GET OUT OF THE WAY.

I KNOW YOU'RE IN HERE... YOU SET OFF THE SILENT ALARM.

IT DON'T CALL THE COPS, IT CALLS ME.

COPS WILL JUST TOSS YOU IN JAIL.

ME...

I GET TO SHOOT YOUR SORRY ASS.

COME OUT NOW... SHOW YOURSELF AND I WON'T SHOOT.

KLANG!

BOOM!

KLANG!

BOOM!

HONK!

VROOOM!

ABSTRACT STUDIO
ISSUE NO.
22
3.99 US

TERRY MOORE

RACHEL RISING

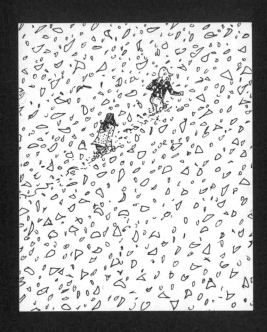

"WE BURY THINGS SO DEEP WE NO LONGER
REMEMBER THERE WAS ANYTHING TO BURY.
OUR BODIES REMEMBER. OUR NEUROTIC STATES
REMEMBER. BUT WE DON'T."
—JEANETTE WINTERSON

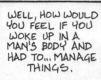

EVERYTHING COME OUT OKAY?

UHMM, YES.

NO PROBLEMS?

NO.

ROOM

OKAY, SO,... ≡COUGH!≡ WHAT'S THE PLAN?

YOU'RE BLUSHING.

WELL, HOW WOULD YOU FEEL IF YOU WOKE UP IN A MAN'S BODY AND HAD TO... MANAGE THINGS.

OKAY, NO MORE BATHROOM BREAKS FOR YOU! AND... I WANT TO TALK TO JET!

WHAT?

YOU HEARD ME. I WANT TO TALK TO JET—RIGHT NOW! I KNOW SHE'S IN THERE.

UH...

BRYN, I'M NOT SURE WHAT YOU WANT ME TO DO HERE.

JET, IT'S ME, RACHEL! TALK TO ME!

BRYN?

JET, ANSWER ME! WAKE UP, JET! TALK TO ME!

RACHEL?

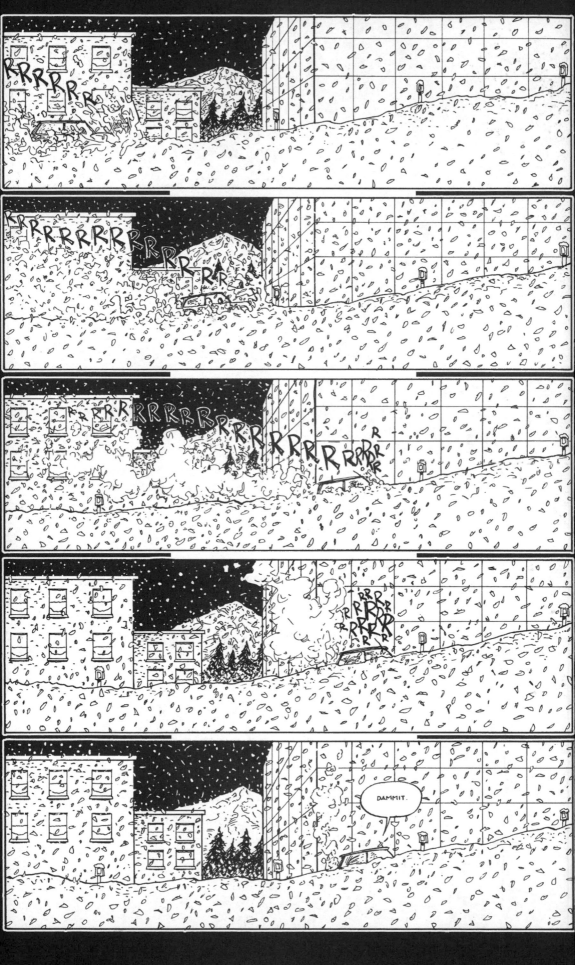

THAT IS A LIGHT YOU CANNOT HIDE, MARY M^cKENNA.

YOUR DAUGHTER SEES THE WORLD DIFFERENTLY, MARY. YOU SEE TREES AND BIRDS AND BODIES... SHE SEES SPIRIT. IT'S A VERY RARE GIFT. WITH YOUR PERMISSION, I'D LIKE TO HELP HER DEVELOP IT.

I'M OFFERING A PLACE WHERE BRYN ERIN WILL BE EDUCATED AND CARED FOR.

A SAFE PLACE.

WICKEDDD!

I WARNED YOU BEFORE, WOMAN—

STAY OFF MY LAND!

YOUR KIND'S NOT WELCOME HERE!

MY KIND?

SILENCE, HARLOT! I KNOW WHAT YOU ARE!

GET THAT FORK OUT OF MY FACE, YOU FOOL.

YOU'RE WICKED!

IF THIS LAND ABHORS THE WICKED, WHY ARE YOU STILL HERE, LUCAS McKENNA?

I SEE THE STRIPES BENEATH YOUR DAUGHTER'S BLOUSE!

IF YOU DIDN'T HAVE SO MANY MOUTHS TO FEED, I'D TAKE YOUR LAST EYE AND EAT IT LIKE AN EGG.

ABSTRACT STUDIO
ISSUE NO.
23
3.99 US
TERRY MOORE
RACHEL RISING

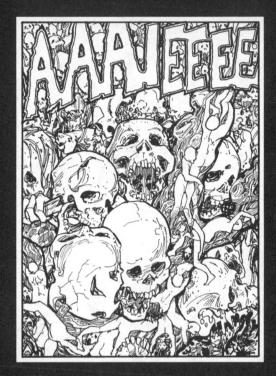

"WE ARE EACH OUR OWN DEVIL,
AND WE MAKE THIS WORLD OUR HELL."
—OSCAR WILDE

WHAT'S THAT?

HMM?

THAT NOISE.

CLUNK CLOK SHHHD CLUNK! CLUK! SHHHD!

SEVEN LOCKS... OPENING INSIDE. THEY'RE TRIGGERED BY A PAIR OF MAGNETS TUNED TO MY ENERGY. WHEN I HOLD MY HANDS LIKE THIS, ON EITHER SIDE...

WATER BASIN CIRCA 1730

CLICK!

POP!

HA! STILL WORKS.

CREAK!

SEE THE TREE SAP YOU NEED FOR JOHNNY?

YES. GOT IT.

DO YOU HAVE A POTION IN THERE TO STOP LILITH?

THERE ISN'T A POTION STRONG ENOUGH TO STOP LILITH.

BUT THIS MIGHT DO THE TRICK.

WELL, ONE THING HASN'T CHANGED SINCE MY TIME— WINTERS HERE ARE STILL BAD.

NO, THEY'RE NOT AS BRUTAL ANYMORE. THIS... THIS IS THE WORK OF YOU KNOW WHO.

WHAT IS SHE TRYING TO DO, BURY THE WHOLE TOWN UNDER SNOW AND FREEZE EVERY-BODY TO DEATH?

WORKED IN JAMESTOWN.

YOU'RE TALKING ABOUT LILITH, RIGHT? YOU THINK THIS IS THE FIRST TIME SHE'S DONE THIS? OCTOBER 31, 1608, VICAR HUNT ACCUSED HER OF BEASTIALITY, SHOT HER HORSE AND FED IT TO HIS CONGREGATION.

THEY DROPPED LILITH INTO THE TRASH HOLE OUTSIDE THE FORT AND LEFT HER THERE. IT TOOK HER 3 DAYS TO CLIMB OUT. SO, SHE DID HER THING— POISONED THE SWAMPY LAND THOSE IDIOTS HAD CHOSEN TO SETTLE AND CALLED UP THE WINTER FROM HELL.

WITHIN 2 YEARS, ALMOST EVERYONE IN THE FORT DIED— STARVED TO DEATH. THE VICAR WAS ONE OF THE FIRST TO DIE.

THE SURVIVORS ATE THE CORPSES — EVEN THE BONES. THEY GROUND THEM INTO POWDER AND MIXED IT INTO A PASTE WITH THEIR OWN PISS AND FECES. ONE MAN KILLED HIS SLEEPING WIFE AND COOKED HER.

HE ATE EVERYTHING BUT THE SKULL. IT WAS TOO THICK.

JOHNNY?

JOHNNY?

ANYBODY HOME?

JOHNNY? IS IT YOU?

:WHINE:

I'VE COME TO GET YOU.

DR. SIEMEN IS FLUSH-ING THE POISON OUT OF YOUR BODY AND RACHEL THINKS SHE CAN PUT YOU BACK IN IT. IS THAT OKAY?

I MEAN...

DO YOU WANT TO TRY IT?

AAAUUGH!

EVERYTHING'S GOING TO BE OKAY, JOHNNY.

I SAW RACHEL PUT YOU IN THERE — I'M SURE SHE CAN GET YOU OUT.

SHE SAVED YOUR LIFE, JOHNNY. SHE CAUGHT YOUR SPIRIT BEFORE IT LEFT FOR GOOD.

I WISH SOMEBODY LOVED ME LIKE THAT.

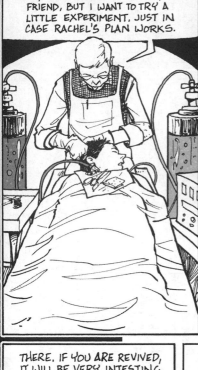

SO, I HOPE YOU DON'T MIND, MY FRIEND, BUT I WANT TO TRY A LITTLE EXPERIMENT. JUST IN CASE RACHEL'S PLAN WORKS.

YOU NEVER KNOW. I ONCE SAW PIGS FLY.

IT TOOK CATAPULTS TO GET THEM UP THERE, BUT FOR A FEW GLORIOUS MOMENTS, PIGS FLEW LIKE EAGLES.

I WISH YOU COULD'VE SEEN IT — THE SKY FILLED WITH SQUEELING PORK — DROPPING LIKE SUICIDE BOMBS ON THE MEDICI ENCAMPMENT.

THERE. IF YOU ARE REVIVED, IT WILL BE VERY INTESTING TO SEE IF THIS WORKS.

I HOPE YOU PULL THROUGH, JOHNNY. I REALLY DO.

I HAVE A CONFESSION TO MAKE, OLD FRIEND. MY WIFE, SYLVIE, ISN'T REALLY AN AGORAPHOBIC — SHE'S DEAD.

SO THE SEX ISN'T WHAT IT USED TO BE. I HAVE TO DO ALL THE WORK AND SOME-THING ALWAYS FALLS OFF, BUT YOU... SO... FRESH...

BRRMMMMM...

UH OH.

TERRY MOORE

ABSTRACT STUDIO
ISSUE NO.
24
3.99 US

RACHEL RISING

"I'M A CHOIR GIRL GONE
HORRIBLY, DESPERATELY WRONG."
—FLORENCE WELCH

DEATH IS NOT THE WORST THING
THAT CAN HAPPEN TO YOU.
—PLATO

The saga continues with a new story arc in issue 25!

READ RACHEL'S
EXTRAORDINARY
STORY FROM
THE BEGINNING...

THE SHADOW
OF DEATH

FEAR NO MALUS

CEMETERY SONGS

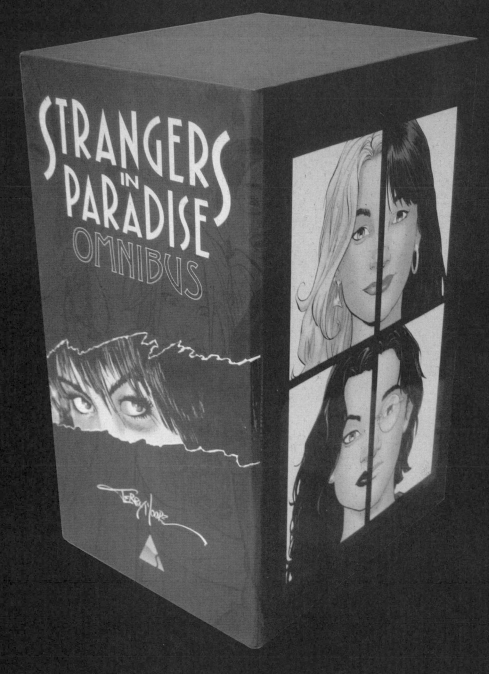

STORY & ART
TERRY MOORE

PUBLISHER
ROBYN MOORE

ABSTRACT STUDIO
BOX 271487
HOUSTON, TEXAS 77277